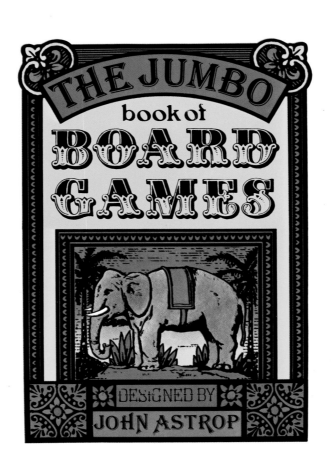

THE JUMBO
book of
BOARD GAMES

DESIGNED BY
JOHN ASTROP

KESTREL BOOKS

KESTREL BOOKS
Published by Penguin Books Ltd
Harmondsworth, Middlesex, England

First published 1979

Reprinted 1979

ISBN 0 7226 5544 4

Printed in Italy

INTRODUCTION

Board games have been enjoyed by people the world over
for thousands of years. In Egypt a version of Nine Men's
Morris has been discovered, cut into roofing slabs which
date back 3,000 years. Pachisi, a forerunner of Ludo, is an
Indian game also thought to be several thousand years old
and traditionally played with beads or shells for counters and
6 cowrie shells for dice (the number of shells falling with their
open sides uppermost indicating the number of squares to
be moved; i.e., 4 open sides up equal a throw of 4). Palm
Tree has its origins in a name known to archaeologists as
Dogs and Jackals because pieces belonging to a similar
board were in the shape of these animals; the pieces, discovered in Thebes, are from about 2000 BC.

During the last century, when printing became cheaper,
many hundreds of attractive and ingenious board games
were produced, frequently with special emphasis on their
educational value. In our century, too, a great number of new
games have been invented. Yet, whatever their age, origin,
or complexity, most board games follow the same basic
principles and may be said to belong to one of three types:
race games (e.g., Ludo, Snakes and Ladders), position
games (Nine Men's Morris, Five Field Kono) and war games
(Chess, Warlord).

In this book we have brought together some old games
and some completely new; games simple enough for a
young child to play, and games of skill and strategy. All can
be played with ordinary counters (for which buttons, pebbles
or small pieces of paper may be substituted – see individual
rules for special requirements of number and colour), and a
single dice (apart from Backgammon which needs 2). Unless
otherwise stated, players should each throw the dice to
decide who starts; with the highest scorer going first, play
clockwise round the table.

The following may serve as a rough guide to help players
choose a game to suit their ages, abilities or whims.

Fire! Fire!, Steeplechase, Ludo, Dragon –
recommended for the youngest players, these games involve
a great deal of luck and little strategy

Palm Tree, Shunting, Jackpot, Space Race –
these are less straightforward to play than those listed above,
but are still largely a matter of luck rather than choice of moves

Nine Men's Morris, Five Field Kono, Asalto –
these position games depend on strategy alone

Spychase, Warlord, Backgammon –
the outcome of these depends on a combination of strategy,
imagination and luck.

PALM TREE

2 players; set of 4 counters each; 1 dice

OBJECT: To be first to get all 4 counters from one side of the tree
trunk to the other

TO PLAY: Place 1 counter on each of 4 dots ranging down from the
top of the tree trunk (first counter on *gold* dot, remaining 3 on
black); one player starts to the left of the tree trunk, the other to the
right. Take turns to move any counter, according to the throw of the
dice. Players move in opposite directions around the chain of dots
(down the trunk, away from it, around the edge of the board, up the
other side of the trunk). Counters may be started on any throw. A
throw of 6 does not gain player a second move.

CONDITIONS: (1) Counters may not move to dot already occupied
by player's own or opponent's counter. (2) Counter landing on:
blue, moves immediately to the linked blue dot (unless that is
already occupied); *red*, misses a turn; *green*, moves back 5 (then,
if it lands on blue, back again to linked blue). (3) If a player cannot
move any counter, opponent uses that throw as well as his own
throw (he may move separate counters with the two throws if he
wishes). If neither player can move, the game is drawn – start
again. End with exact throws to get counters to 4 dots on which
opponent started.

LUDO

2, 3, or 4 players; set of 4 counters each (if possible a set should be in a colour corresponding to one of the board's 4 colours); 1 dice

OBJECT: To be first to get all 4 counters 'home'

TO PLAY: Each player places his 4 counters on matching 4 circles within his own 'base' square. Take turns to throw the dice; a 6 is needed to get any counter from base on to the matching coloured circle outside. The 6 also gains player another throw with which he can start the counter moving, according to the dice throw, in a clockwise direction round the circuit of white squares. One arm of the central cross matches each player's base colour; a counter, having gone round the circuit and arriving at the white square at the end of that arm, travels down the arm to its home triangle. A player landing his counter on top of an opponent's sends the opponent's counter back to its base; from there it can only re-enter the circuit on a throw of 6. Once on its own arm of the cross, a counter is of course safe. Exact number must be thrown to get a counter home; if number is too high, move another counter or miss a turn. Any number of counters may be on the circuit at the same time, provided that a 6 is thrown to get each one on. A throw of 6 always gains player another throw; separate throws in a single turn may be used to move different counters on to or around the circuit.

FIRE! FIRE!   2 or more players; 1 counter each; 1 dice

OBJECT: To be first to reach the top (**92**) and put out the match

TO PLAY: Take turns to move according to dice throw. Race to the top. To land on **92**, exact number must be thrown; if number is too high, miss a turn.

ADVENTURES ON THE WAY (numbered in black):

3 – up to 25	46 – up to 69	80 – down to 10
7 – up to 35	53 – down to 5	82 – down to 27
39 – along to 41	65 – along to 67	86 – down to 62
44 – down to 21	72 – along to 77	90 – down to 20
45 – down to 1	74 – up to 88	

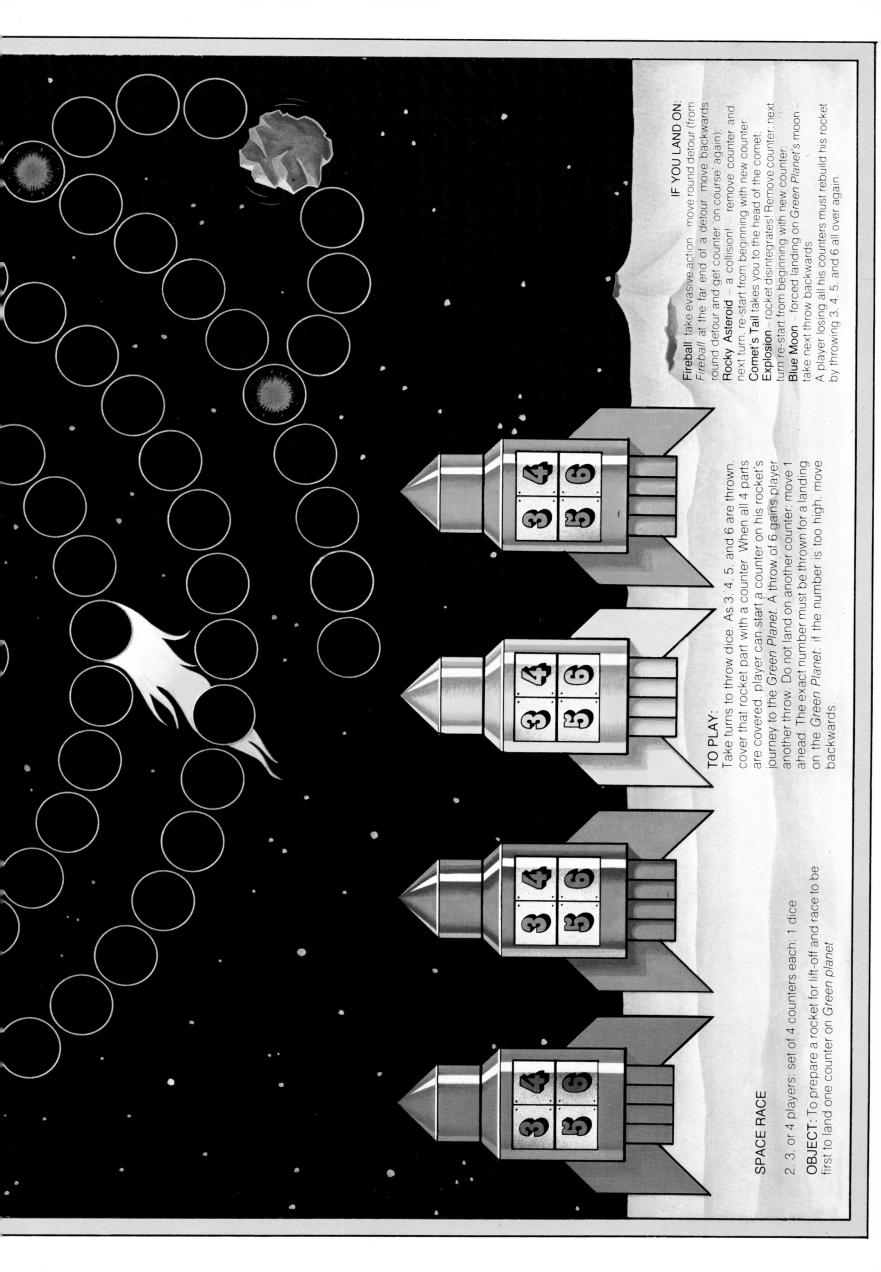

IF YOU LAND ON:

Fireball: take evasive action – move round detour (from *Fireball* at the far end of a detour, move backwards round detour and get counter 'on course' again).

Rocky Asteroid – a collision! – remove counter and next turn, re-start from beginning with new counter.

Comet's Tail takes you to the head of the comet.

Explosion – rocket disintegrates! Remove counter: next turn re-start from beginning with new counter.

Blue Moon – forced landing on *Green Planet's* moon – take next turn throw backwards.

A player losing all his counters must rebuild his rocket by throwing 3, 4, 5, and 6 all over again.

TO PLAY:

Take turns to throw dice. As 3, 4, 5, and 6 are thrown, cover that rocket part with a counter. When all 4 parts are covered, player can start a counter on his rocket's journey to the *Green Planet*. A throw of 6 gains player another throw. Do not land on another counter: move 1 ahead. The exact number must be thrown for a landing on the *Green Planet*: if the number is too high, move backwards.

SPACE RACE

2, 3, or 4 players: set of 4 counters each: 1 dice

OBJECT: To prepare a rocket for lift-off and race to be first to land one counter on *Green planet*

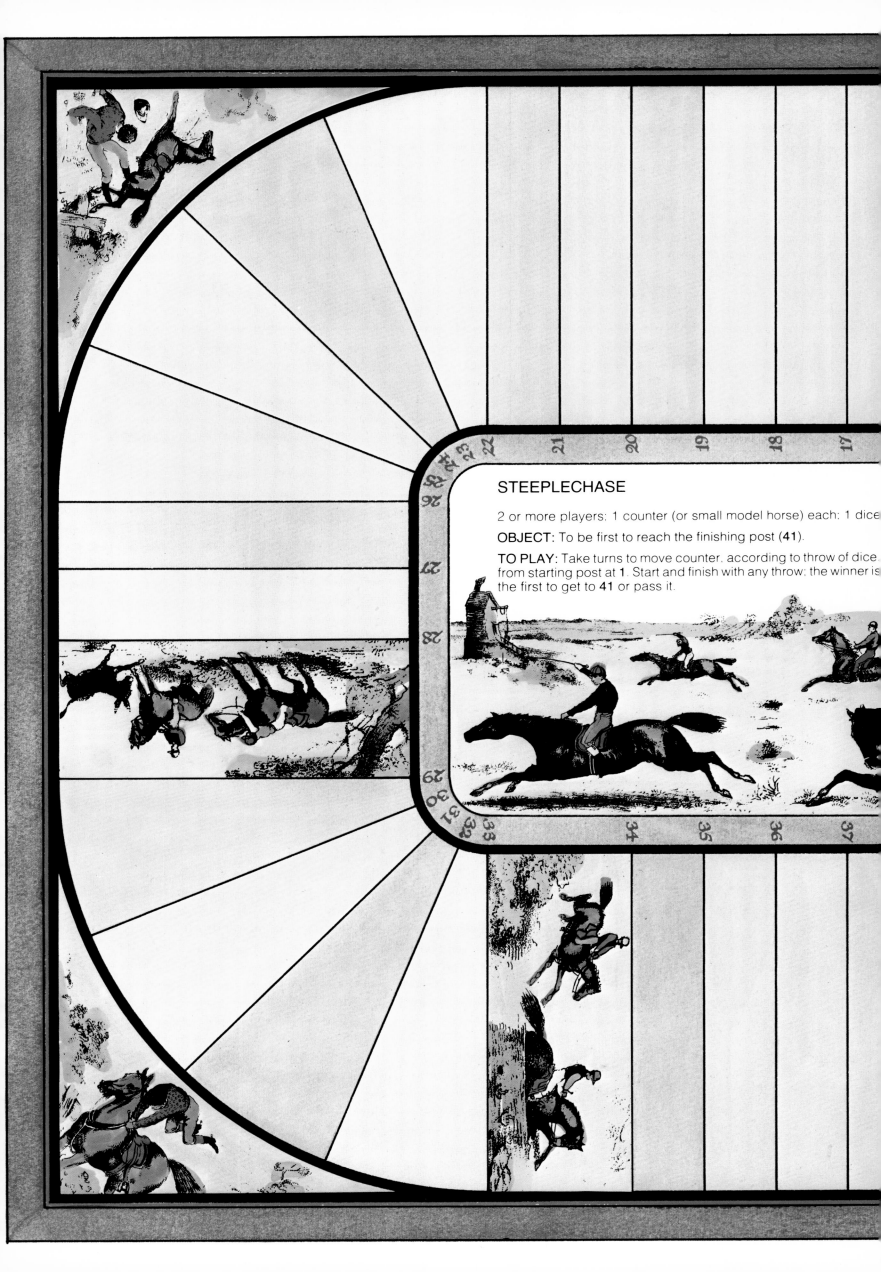

STEEPLECHASE

2 or more players: 1 counter (or small model horse) each: 1 dice

OBJECT: To be first to reach the finishing post (**41**).

TO PLAY: Take turns to move counter. according to throw of dice. from starting post at **1**. Start and finish with any throw: the winner is the first to get to **41** or pass it.

17 18 19 20 21 22 23 24 25 26 27 28 29 30 31 32 33 34 35 36 37

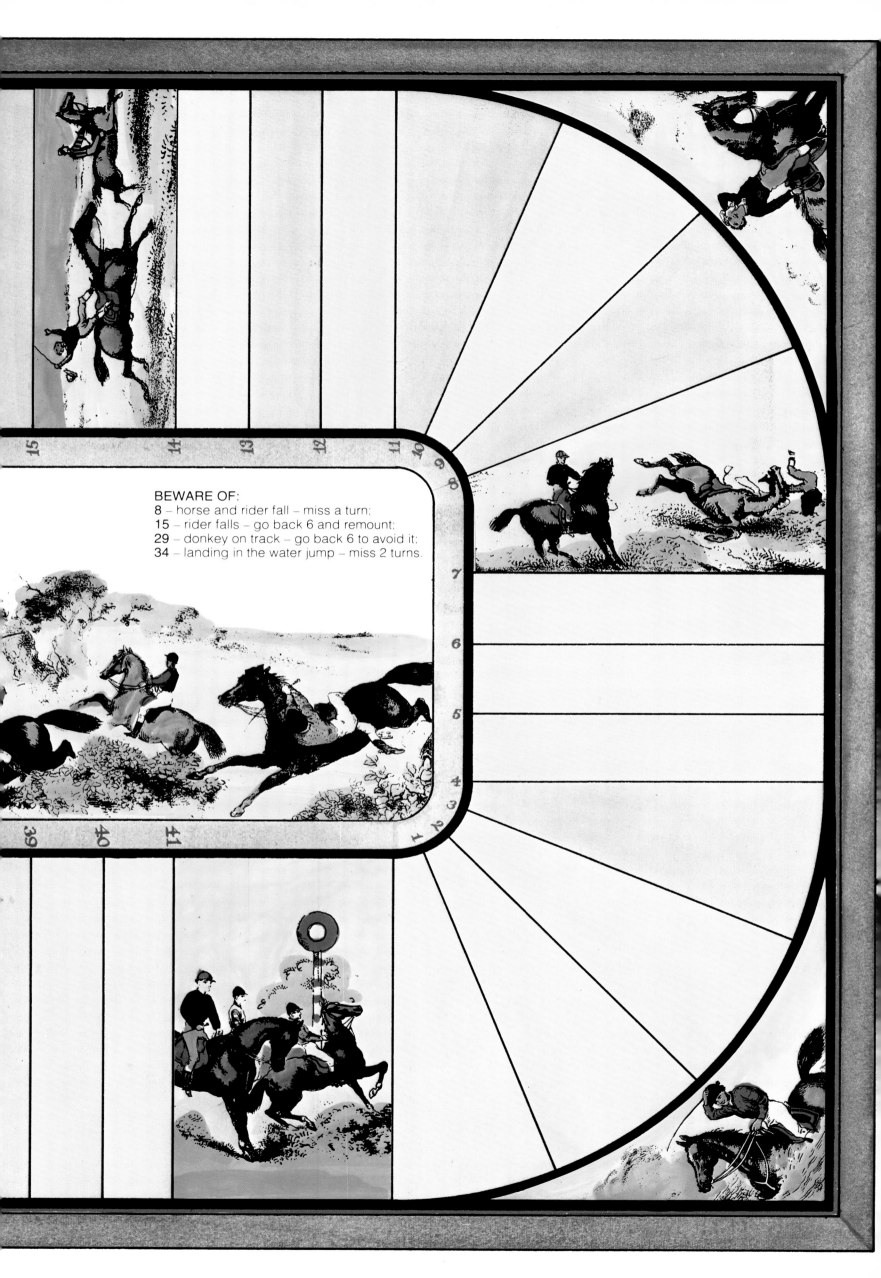

BEWARE OF:
8 – horse and rider fall – miss a turn;
15 – rider falls – go back 6 and remount;
29 – donkey on track – go back 6 to avoid it;
34 – landing in the water jump – miss 2 turns.

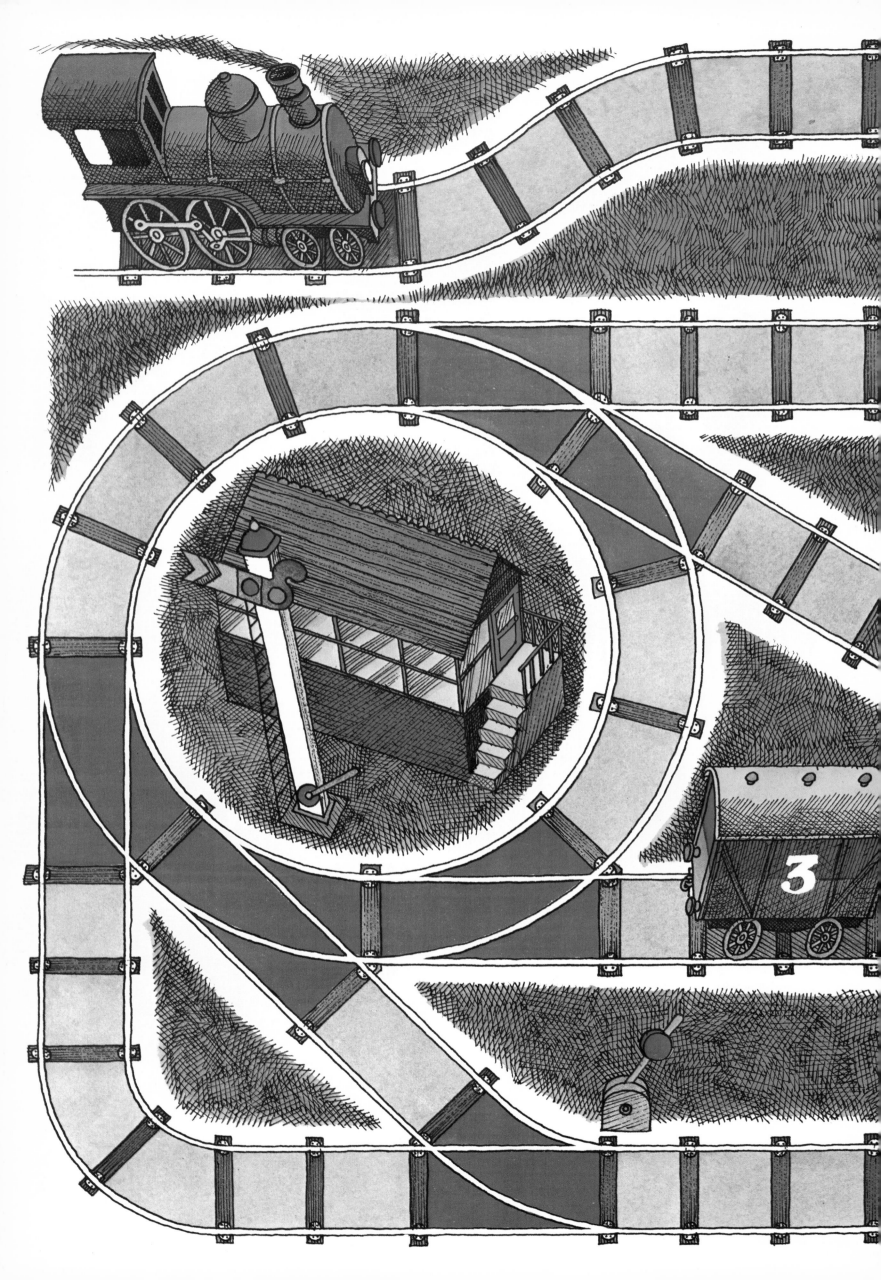

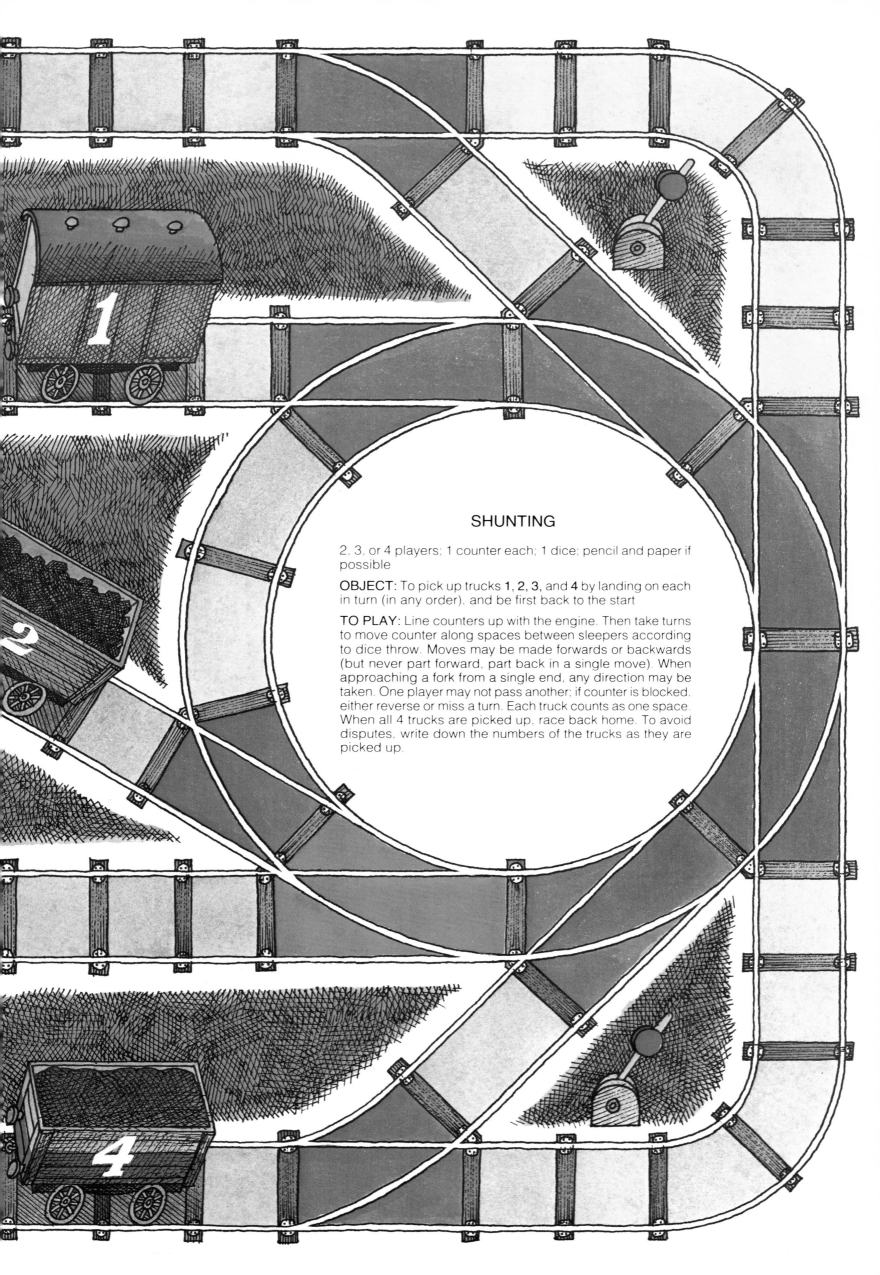

SHUNTING

2, 3, or 4 players; 1 counter each; 1 dice; pencil and paper if possible

OBJECT: To pick up trucks **1, 2, 3,** and **4** by landing on each in turn (in any order), and be first back to the start

TO PLAY: Line counters up with the engine. Then take turns to move counter along spaces between sleepers according to dice throw. Moves may be made forwards or backwards (but never part forward, part back in a single move). When approaching a fork from a single end, any direction may be taken. One player may not pass another; if counter is blocked, either reverse or miss a turn. Each truck counts as one space. When all 4 trucks are picked up, race back home. To avoid disputes, write down the numbers of the trucks as they are picked up.

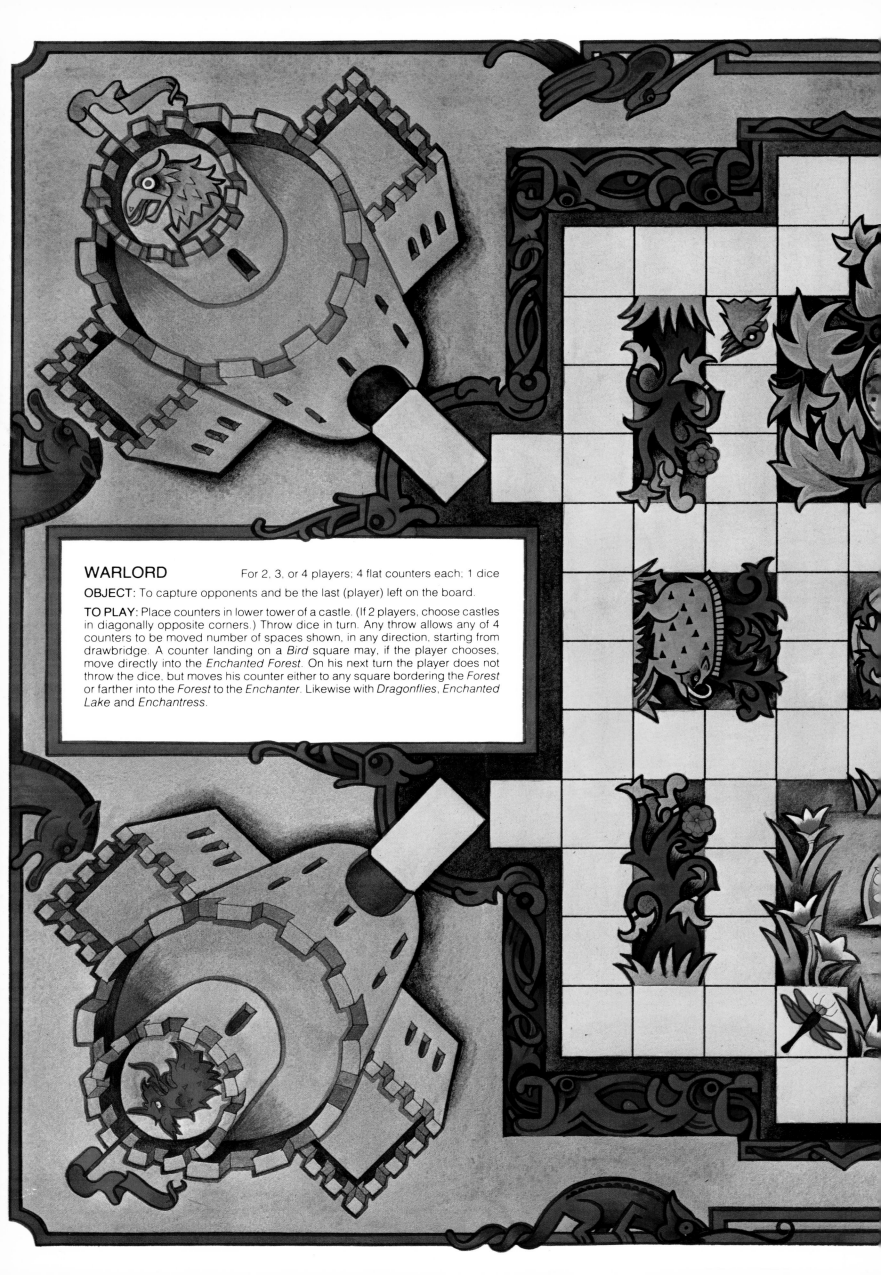

WARLORD

For 2, 3, or 4 players; 4 flat counters each; 1 dice

OBJECT: To capture opponents and be the last (player) left on the board.

TO PLAY: Place counters in lower tower of a castle. (If 2 players, choose castles in diagonally opposite corners.) Throw dice in turn. Any throw allows any of 4 counters to be moved number of spaces shown, in any direction, starting from drawbridge. A counter landing on a *Bird* square may, if the player chooses, move directly into the *Enchanted Forest*. On his next turn the player does not throw the dice, but moves his counter either to any square bordering the *Forest* or farther into the *Forest* to the *Enchanter*. Likewise with *Dragonflies*, *Enchanted Lake* and *Enchantress*.

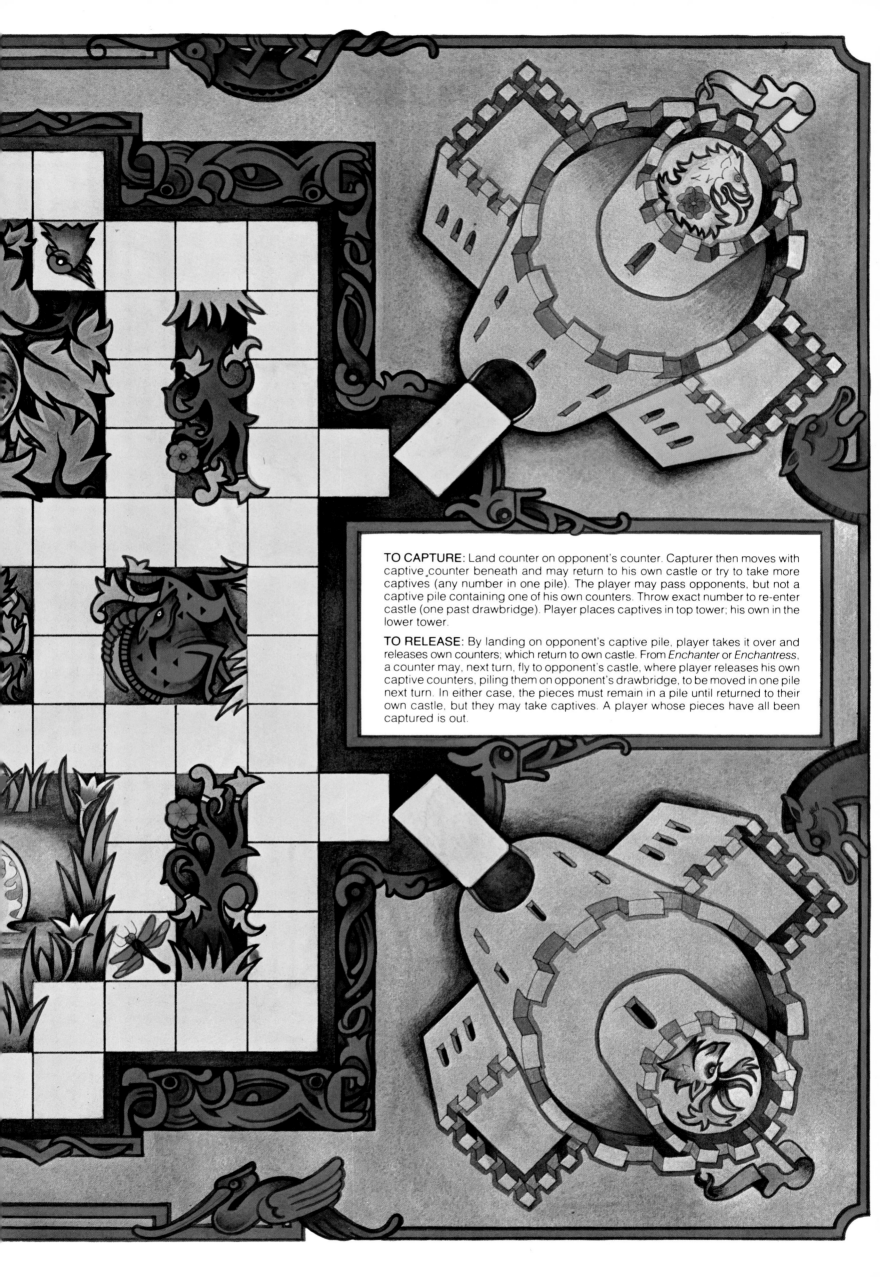

TO CAPTURE: Land counter on opponent's counter. Capturer then moves with captive counter beneath and may return to his own castle or try to take more captives (any number in one pile). The player may pass opponents, but not a captive pile containing one of his own counters. Throw exact number to re-enter castle (one past drawbridge). Player places captives in top tower; his own in the lower tower.

TO RELEASE: By landing on opponent's captive pile, player takes it over and releases own counters; which return to own castle. From *Enchanter* or *Enchantress*, a counter may, next turn, fly to opponent's castle, where player releases his own captive counters, piling them on opponent's drawbridge, to be moved in one pile next turn. In either case, the pieces must remain in a pile until returned to their own castle, but they may take captives. A player whose pieces have all been captured is out.

DRAGON

2 or more players; 1 counter each; 1 dice

OBJECT: To be first to reach the *Pagoda*

TO PLAY: Take turns to move around the squares according to the dice throw. A throw of 6 gains player another throw. To reach the *Pagoda* the exact number must be thrown; if the number is too large, miss a turn.

ON THE WAY, IF YOU LAND ON:
the *Chinese* characters on green squares, move any other player back 3;
the *Princess*, move any other player to square above her to hear the music;
the *Magician*, change places with any other player, or move on 6;
the *Dragon's Tail* (any square it crosses), go back 3.

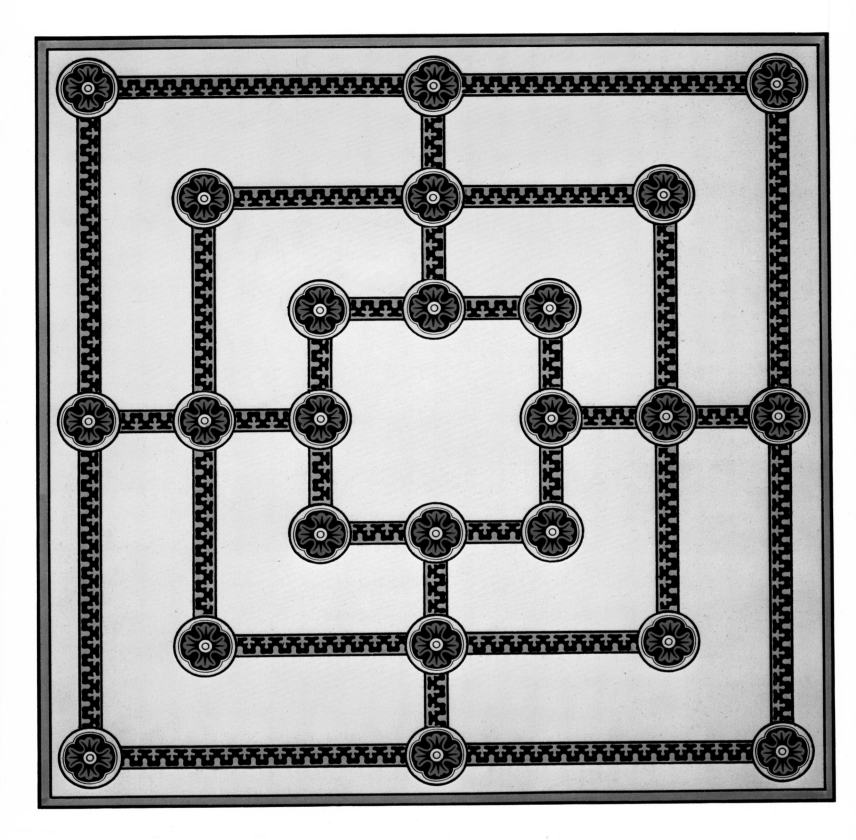

NINE MEN'S MORRIS

2 players; set of 9 counters each

OBJECT: To capture all but 2 of opponent's pieces, or make it impossible for opponent to move

PLACING: Take turns to place a piece at a time at any point of intersection not already occupied. Each player tries to form a 'mill' by getting 3 pieces in a row along any marked line. Whenever a player forms a mill, he removes from the board one of his opponent's pieces – not one that is part of a mill, unless no other piece is available.

MOVING: When all 18 pieces have been played, try to form new mills by moving pieces from existing positions to any adjoining vacant intersection. Players may open an existing mill, move a piece one place to form a new mill, and then re-form the old mill again; each mill formation entitles a player to remove one of his opponent's pieces from the board.

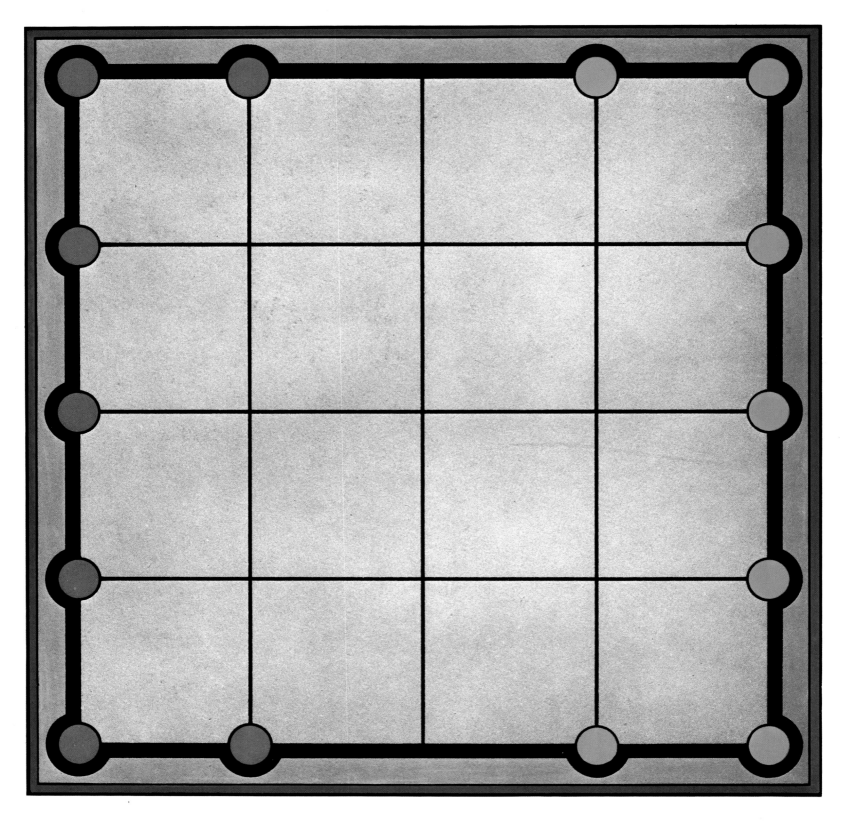

FIVE FIELD KONO

2 players: set of 7 counters each

OBJECT: To be first to get all 7 counters from the coloured dots on one side of the board to those on the opposite side

TO PLAY: One player places a counter on each of the 7 red dots; the other places his counters on the blue dots. Players then take turns to move any one of their counters diagonally across one square. Counters move forwards or backwards to any point of intersection, provided that point is vacant; they may never move more than one square at a time; no counter may land on top of another. The player starting on the blue dots finishes on the red, and vice versa.

SPYCHASE

2, 3, or 4 players; 4 counters (5 when 3 players); 1 dice

OBJECT: For Spy, to steal a set of *plans* and then escape to the *airport* or to the *docks*; for Police, to capture Spy

TO START: Each player throws dice in turn; highest scorer is Spy, rest are Police. Order of play, Spy – Police – Police – Police. Spy places counter on any square. Police then in turn place theirs wherever they wish as long as they do not block Spy in completely.

MOVES: These are made according to the dice throw, in any vertical or horizontal direction along avenues; players cannot choose not to move. A throw of 6 gains player another throw. A counter landing on the end square of a *yellow freeway* may, if player chooses, pass immediately to the opposite end of that freeway.

SPY: cannot pass a Police counter. When he lands on a square bordering one of the 3 sets of *plans*, he may, if he wishes, move inside and steal it. At next throw he can move from any square bordering the *plans*. He must then try to escape by landing with an exact dice throw on either of the two arrowed gates at the *docks* or *airport*.

POLICE: may pass each other or Spy, but may not land on the same square. Until Spy has stolen the *plans*, Police must leave him at least one avenue of escape. Once *plans* have been stolen, Police try to capture Spy by placing their counters so that he cannot move his dice throw. Police may land on a gate.

NB: When only 2 players, 1 player moves 3 Police counters; when 3 players, 2 players move 2 Police counters each.

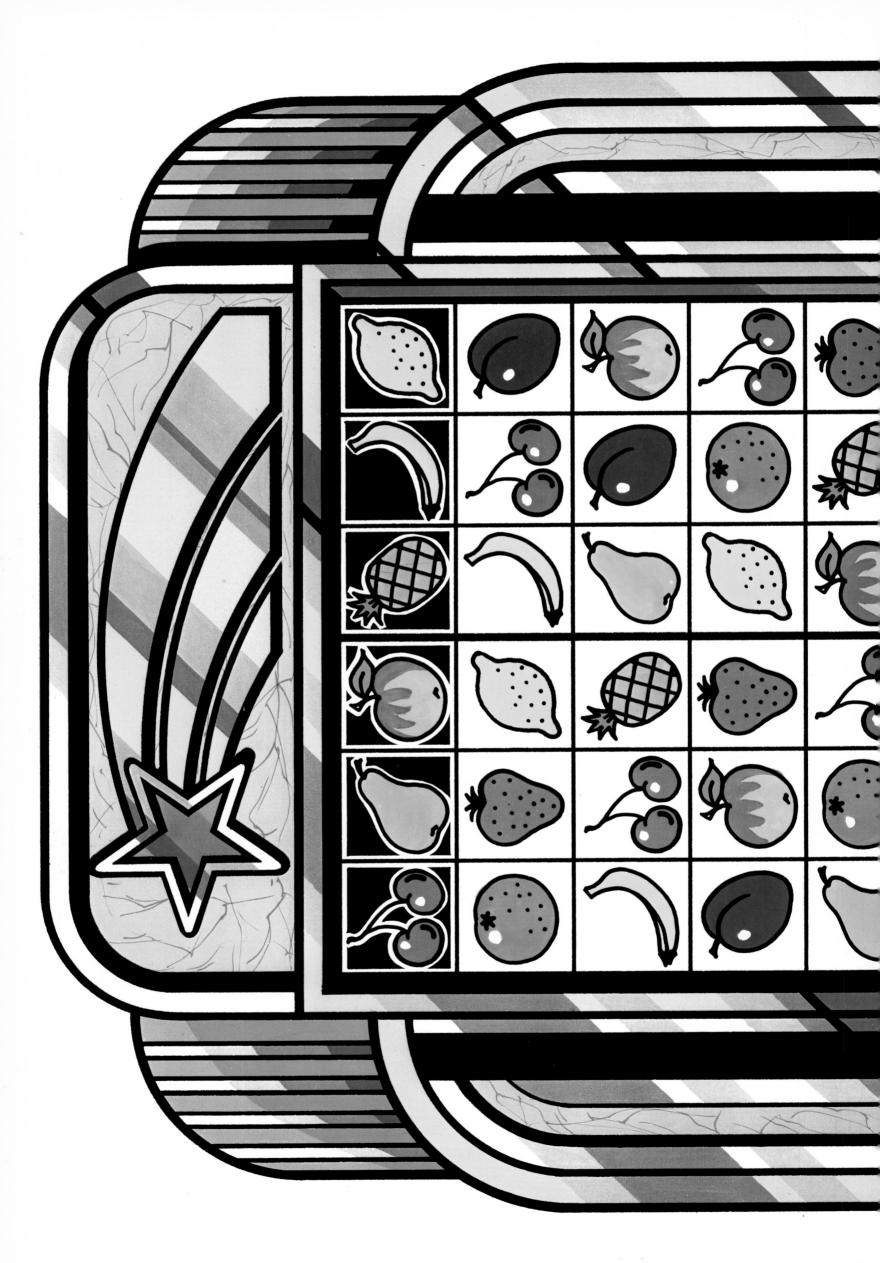

JACKPOT

2 players; 3 counters each; 1 dice

OBJECT: To be first to get all 3 counters on to black fruit squares across top; or – Jackpot – all 3 counters on squares showing same fruit (e.g., lemon – lemon – lemon).

CONDITIONS: (1) Fruit of square a counter leaves must appear on one of the five squares to right or left across the line on which it lands. **(2)** If no counter can be moved up, leading counter must be moved correct number of squares down, no matter what square it lands on. **(3)** If neither 1 nor 2 are possible, miss a turn. **(4)** Once on a black square, a counter cannot be moved again.

TO PLAY: Place counters across bottom row of fruit squares above arrows, one player to right of centre line, the other to left. Take turns to move any counter according to dice throw, up or down lines only (never across).

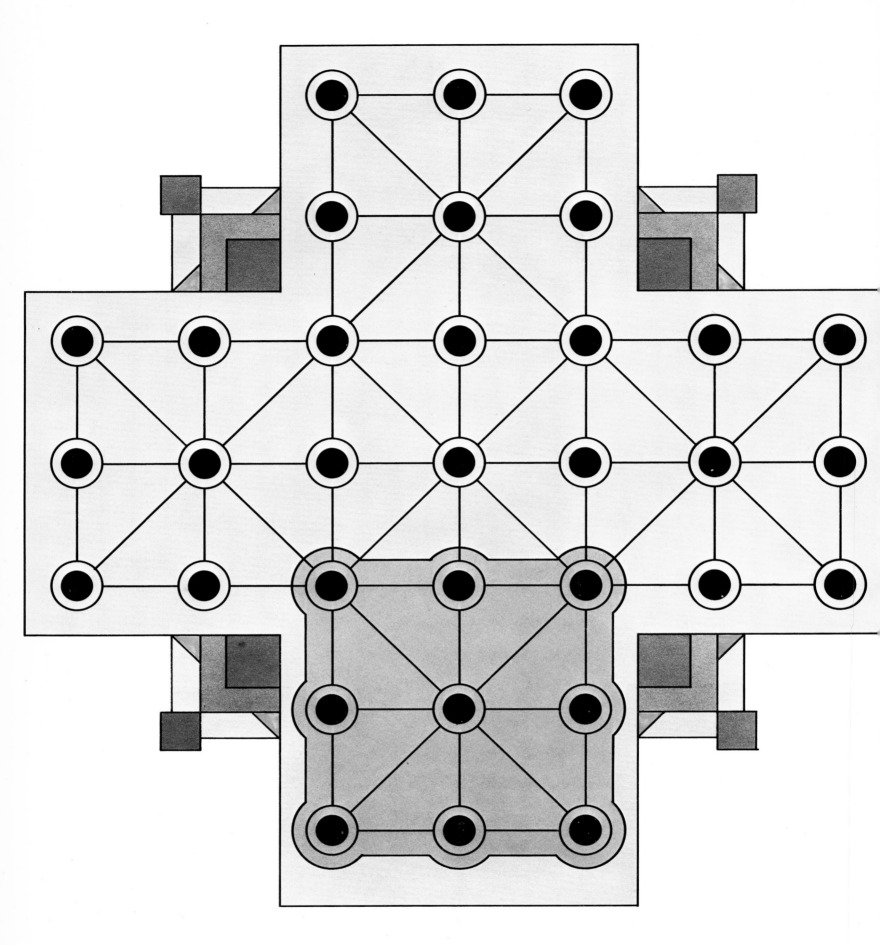

ASALTO

2 players; 26 counters (24 Mutineers in one set, 2 Officers in the other)

OBJECT: For Mutineers, to occupy every point in the fort, or to trap Officers by leaving no point on to which they can move; for Officers, to capture so many Mutineers that those remaining (9) are too few to trap them

TO START: Decide which player is to be Officers, which Mutineers. Officers may be placed on any 2 points in the **fort** (represented by the 9 points at the bottom of the board); Mutineers cover all points outside the **fort**.

TO PLAY: Take turns to move a piece from point to point along any connecting line. Mutineers may only move towards the **fort** and one point at a time. Officers may move in any direction, and capture Mutineers by jumping over them to any adjacent vacant point; the captive Mutineer is then removed from the board. Officers must jump whenever possible, or be removed from the board. Several Mutineers can be captured in one move provided that there is an empty point for the Officer to jump to next to each captive.

BACKGAMMON

2 players; set of 15 counters each; 2 dice

OBJECT: To be first to take all 15 counters off the board

TO PLAY: Set up counters according to diagram. Throwing alternately, each player uses both dice, moving one counter the number of spaces shown on one dice, then the same, or another, counter according to the other dice. A double gives a player 4 moves, with each of which any counter is moved the number of spaces shown on one dice – e.g. a double 5 gives 4 moves of 5 spaces. At all times players must move if they can. A counter may not land on a space already occupied by 2 or more of opponent's counters. A counter is 'taken' if it is alone on a space and opponent's counter lands on that space. To bring a taken counter back into the game, player must throw the number of a space in opponent's home which is not occupied by more than

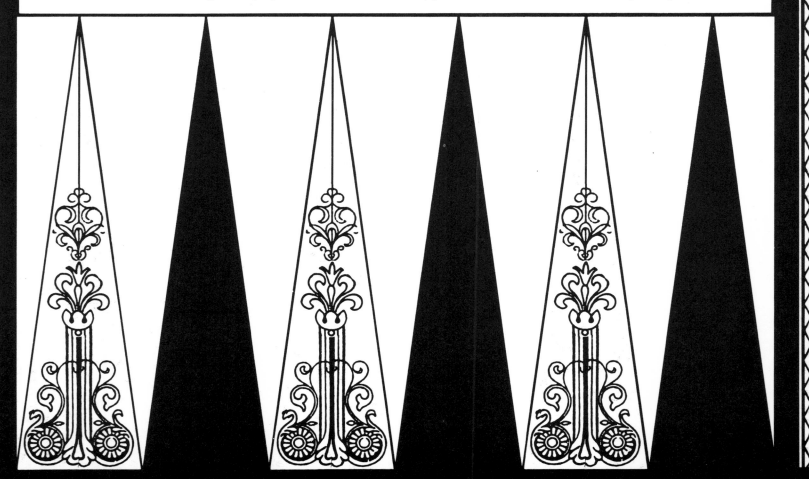